D1262976

Walt and Vic Johnson
We love you,
    John, Ann, Stuart, Clark
        and "Cocke"

May, 1965

MY BRIMFUL BOOK

FAVORITE POEMS OF CHILDHOOD

MOTHER GOOSE RHYMES

ANIMAL STORIES

Edited by DANA BRUCE

Illustrated by

TASHA TUDOR

MARGOT AUSTIN

WESLEY DENNIS

PLATT & MUNK, *Publishers*

NEW YORK

Copyright © 1960.

The Platt & Munk Co., Inc. New York 10, N.Y.

All rights in this book are reserved. No copyrighted material in this book
may be reproduced or used in any manner without written permission of
the publisher, except by a reviewer who, with proper credit, may quote brief
passages and reproduce not more than three illustrations in a review to be pub-
lished in a newspaper or magazine or to be broadcast by radio or television.

Printed in the United States of America.

Library of Congress Catalog Card Number: 60-9213

Contents

Preface

This handsome edition of *My Brimful Book* is joyously filled with words and illustrations that every child will cherish a lifetime. Here are handsomely told poems and rhymes and stories, warmly and colorfully depicted by three outstanding artists of our time. Love and care and conscientious effort have gone into every line and every page. Truly, *My Brimful Book* is filled to the brim with the wealth that is dearest to the hearts of children.

In a real sense, the content of *My Brimful Book* is timeless. Every child will respond eagerly to Mother Goose Rhymes, Favorite Poems of Childhood, and to Animal Stories, when they are read to him aloud or when he curls up in a quiet corner to read alone. *My Brimful Book* will be a frequent choice, a vital and important part of all his growing-up years.

How could it be otherwise when here will be found such favorite poets as Robert Louis Stevenson and Eugene Field, Christina Rosetti and Clement Moore, Jane Taylor and Henry Wadsworth Longfellow? To these poems have been added the sensitive touch and gentle warmth of Tasha Tudor's illustrations which retain the classical flavor.

And here too are memorable Mother Goose rhymes, some dating back to the Sixteenth Century, the origin of all a rhythmic riddle. Who was Mother Goose—an elderly English flower vendor from Oxford town, as some contend, or a French noblewoman, or that remarkable Boston lady, Elizabeth Vergoose? No matter; Margot Austin's illustrations infuse a new and lasting delight.

To this collection also is added the strong hand of Wesley Dennis. In the world of childhood, animals play an important part. The innate dignity and kindliness and humor of the animal world evokes a similar response in children. Dennis's illustrations deepen the meaning of the stories about animal life told in *My Brimful Book*.

In short, here is a volume of a high order of quality, offered in the earnest belief that an awareness and appreciation of quality, offered to children today, is tomorrow's standard of all good things.

Favorite Poems

of Childhood

Illustrated by Tasha Tudor

At the Seaside

By ROBERT LOUIS STEVENSON

When I was down beside the sea

A wooden spade they gave to me

To dig the sandy shore.

My holes were empty like a cup,

In every hole the sea came up,

Till it could come no more.

Who Has Seen the Wind?

By CHRISTINA G. ROSSETTI

Who has seen the wind?
    Neither I nor you:
But when the leaves hang trembling
    The wind is passing through.

Who has seen the wind?
    Neither you nor I:
But when the trees bow down their heads
    The wind is passing by.

The Star   By JANE TAYLOR

Twinkle, twinkle, little star,
How I wonder what you are,
Up above the world so high,
Like a diamond in the sky.

When the blazing sun is set,
And the grass with dew is wet,
Then you show your little light,
Twinkle, twinkle, all the night.

Then the traveler in the dark
Thanks you for your tiny spark;
He could not see which way to go
If you did not twinkle so.

In the dark blue sky you keep,
And often through my curtains peep,
For you never shut your eye
Till the sun is in the sky.

As your bright and tiny spark
Lights the traveler in the dark,
Though I know not what you are,
Twinkle, twinkle, little star.

Baby By GEORGE MacDONALD

Where did you come from, baby dear?
Out of the everywhere into the here.

Where did you get those eyes so blue?
Out of the sky as I came through.

What makes the light in them sparkle
and spin?
Some of the starry spikes left in.

Where did you find that little tear?
I found it waiting when I got here.

What makes your forehead so smooth
and high?
A soft hand stroked it as I went by.

What makes your cheek like a warm
white rose?
*I saw something better than anyone
knows.*

Whence that three-cornered smile of
bliss?
Three angels gave me at once a kiss.

Where did you get this pearly ear?
God spoke, and it came out to hear.

Where did you get those arms and hands?
Love made itself into hooks and bands.

Feet, whence did you come, you darling
things?
From the same box as the cherubs' wings.

How did they all just come to be you?
God thought about me, and so I grew.

But how did you come to us, you dear?
God thought about you, and so I am here.

The Months

By RICHARD B. SHERIDAN

January snowy,
February flowy,
March blowy;

April showery,
May flowery,
June bowery;

July moppy,
August croppy,
September poppy;

October breezy,
November wheezy,
December freezy.

The Arrow and The Song

By HENRY WADSWORTH LONGFELLOW

I shot an arrow into the air,
It fell to earth, I knew not where;
For, so swiftly it flew, the sight
Could not follow it in its flight.

I breathed a song into the air,
It fell to earth, I knew not where;
For who has sight so keen and strong,
That it can follow the flight of song?

Long, long afterward, in an oak
I found the arrow, still unbroke;
And the song, from beginning to end,
I found again in the heart of a friend.

The Table and the Chair

By EDWARD LEAR

Said the Table to the Chair,
"You can hardly be aware
How I suffer from the heat
And from chilblains on my feet.
If we took a little walk,
We might have a little talk;
Pray let us take the air."
Said the Table to the Chair.

Said the Chair unto the Table,
"Now, you *know* we are not able:
How foolishly you talk,
When you know we *cannot* walk!"
Said the Table with a sigh,
"It can do no harm to try.
I've as many legs as you:
Why can't we walk on two?"

So they both went slowly down,
And walked about the town
With a cheerful bumpy sound
As they toddled round and round;
And everybody cried,
As they hastened to their side,
"See! the Table and the Chair
Have come to take the air!"

But in going down an alley,
To a castle in a valley,
They completely lost their way,
And wandered all the day;
Till, to see them safely back,
They paid a Ducky-quack,
And a Beetle, and a Mouse
Who took them to their house.

Then they whispered to each other,
"O delightful little brother,
What a lovely walk we've taken!
Let us dine on beans and bacon."
So the Ducky and the leetle
Browny-Mousy and the Beetle
Dined, and danced upon their heads
Till they toddled to their beds.

Babyland   By GEORGE COOPER

Which is the way to Babyland?
  Anyone can tell:
  Up one flight,
  To your right;
  Please to ring the bell.

  What can you see in Babyland?
    Little folks in white—
    Downy heads,
    Cradle-beds,
    Faces pure and bright.

    What do they say in Babyland?
      Why, the oddest things!
      Might as well
      Try to tell
      What a birdie sings!

      Who is the queen of Babyland?
        Mother, kind and sweet;
        And her love,
        Born above,
        Guides the little feet.

Pussy Willow

By KATE L. BROWN

Pussy Willow wakened
    From her winter nap,
For the frolic spring breeze
    On her door would tap.

"It is chilly weather
    Though the sun feels good.
I will wrap up warmly,
    Wear my furry hood."

Mistress Pussy Willow
    Opened wide her door.
Never had the sunshine
    Seemed so bright before.

Never had the brooklet
    Seemed so full of cheer:
"Good morning, Pussy Willow,
    Welcome to you, dear!"

Never guest was quainter:
    Pussy came to town
In a hood of silver gray
    And a coat of brown.

Happy little children
    Cried with laugh and shout,
"Spring is coming, coming,
    Pussy Willow's out."

A Visit from St. Nicholas

By CLEMENT C. MOORE

'Twas the night before Christmas, when all through the house
Not a creature was stirring, not even a mouse;
The stockings were hung by the chimney with care,
In hopes that St. Nicholas soon would be there;
The children were nestled all snug in their beds,
While visions of sugar-plums danced through their heads;
And Mamma in her kerchief, and I in my cap,
Had just settled our brains for a long winter's nap,
When out on the lawn there arose such a clatter,
I sprang from my bed to see what was the matter.

Away to the window I flew like a flash,
Tore open the shutters and threw up the sash.
The moon on the breast of the new-fallen snow
Gave the luster of midday to objects below,
When, what to my wondering eyes should appear,
But a miniature sleigh, and eight tiny reindeer,
With a little old driver, so lively and quick,
I knew in a moment it must be St. Nick.
More rapid than eagles his coursers they came,
And he whistled, and shouted, and called them by name:
"Now, Dasher! now, Dancer! now, Prancer! and Vixen!
On, Comet! on, Cupid! on Donder and Blitzen!
To the top of the porch! to the top of the wall!
Now dash away! dash away! dash away all!"

As dry leaves that before the wild hurricane fly,
When they meet with an obstacle, mount to the sky,
So up to the housetop the coursers they flew,
With a sleigh full of toys, and St. Nicholas too.
And then, in a twinkling, I heard on the roof
The prancing and pawing of each little hoof.
As I drew in my head, and was turning around,
Down the chimney St. Nicholas came with a bound.

He was dressed all in fur, from his head to his foot,
And his clothes were all tarnished with ashes and soot;
A bundle of toys he had flung on his back,
And he looked like a peddler just opening his pack.
His eyes how they twinkled! his dimples how merry!
His cheeks were like roses, his nose like a cherry!
His droll little mouth was drawn up like a bow,
And the beard of his chin was as white as the snow;
The stump of a pipe he held tight in his teeth,
And the smoke it encircled his head like a wreath;
He had a broad face and a little round belly
That shook, when he laughed, like a bowlful of jelly.

He was chubby and plump, a right jolly old elf,
And I laughed when I saw him, in spite of myself;
A wink of his eye and a twist of his head,
Soon gave me to know I had nothing to dread.
He spoke not a word, but went straight to his work,
And filled all the stockings; then turned with a jerk,
And laying his finger aside of his nose,
And giving a nod, up the chimney he rose;
He sprang to his sleigh, to the team gave a whistle,
And away they all flew like the down of a thistle,
But I heard him exclaim, ere he drove out of sight,
"Happy Christmas to all and to all a good night!"

The Rock-a-by Lady

By EUGENE FIELD

The Rock-a-by Lady from Hushaby Street
    Comes stealing; comes creeping;
The poppies they hang from her head to her feet,
And each hath a dream that is tiny and fleet—
She bringeth her poppies to you, my sweet,
    When she findeth you sleeping!

There is one little dream of a beautiful drum—
    "Rub-a-dub!" it goeth;
There is one little dream of a big sugar-plum,
And lo! thick and fast the other dreams come
Of popguns that bang, and tin tops that hum
    And a trumpet that bloweth!

And dollies peep out of those wee little dreams
    With laughter and singing;
And boats go a-floating on silvery streams,
And the stars peek-a-boo with their own
        misty gleams,
And up, up, and up, where the Mother
        Moon beams,
The fairies go winging!

Would you dream all these dreams that are
        tiny and fleet?
    They'll come to you sleeping;
So shut the two eyes that are weary, my sweet,
For the Rock-a-by Lady from Hushaby Street,
With poppies that hang from her head to her feet,
    Comes stealing; comes creeping.

The Slumber Boat

By ALICE C. D. RILEY

Baby's boat's the silver moon,
Sailing in the sky,
Sailing o'er the sea of sleep,
While the clouds float by.

Sail, baby, sail,
Out upon that sea,
Only don't forget to sail,
Back again to me.

Baby's fishing for a dream,
Fishing near and far,
His line a silver moonbeam is,
His bait a silver star.

Sail, baby, sail,
Out upon that sea,
Only don't forget to sail,
Back again to me.

Mother Goose Rhymes

Illustrated by Margot Austin

SEE-SAW, Margery Daw,
Jacky shall have a new master.
Jacky shall have but a penny a day,
Because he can't work any faster.

CURLY locks, Curly locks, wilt thou
    be mine?
Thou shalt not wash dishes, nor yet
    feed the swine;
But sit on a cushion and sew a fine
    seam,
And feed upon strawberries, sugar,
    and cream.

HOT-CROSS buns! Hot-cross buns!
One a penny, two a penny,
    Hot-cross buns.
If you have no daughters,
Give them to your sons,
One a penny, two a penny,
    Hot-cross buns.

TOMMY'S tears and Mary's fears
Will make them old before their years.

Sing a song of sixpence,
    A pocket full of rye;
Four-and-twenty blackbirds,
    Baked in a pie.

When the pie was opened,
    The birds began to sing;
Was not that a dainty dish,
    To set before the king?

The king was in his counting-house,
    Counting out his money;
The queen was in the parlor,
    Eating bread and honey.

The maid was in the garden,
    Hanging out the clothes;
Down came a blackbird,
    And pecked off her nose.

© THE PLATT & MUNK CO. INC.

HUSH-A-BYE, baby, on the tree top,
    When the wind blows,
    The cradle will rock,
    When the bough bends,
    The cradle will fall,
Down will come baby, cradle, and all.

COME hither, sweet robin,
And be not afraid,
I would not hurt even a feather;
Come hither, sweet robin,
And pick up some bread,
To feed you this very cold weather.

BOW — wow — wow,
    Whose dog art thou?
    Little Tommy Tinker's dog,
    Bow — wow — wow.

LITTLE Bo-Peep has lost her sheep,
    And can't tell where to find them;
Leave them alone, and they'll come
        home,
    Wagging their tails behind them.

HANDY-Spandy, Jack-a-dandy,
Loves plum-cake and sugar-candy.
He bought some at a grocer's shop,
And out he came, hop—hop—hop.

IF I HAD a pony
And he would not go,
Do you think I'd whip him?
    No, no, no!
I'd say, "Gee-up, pony!"
And away he'd go.

I HAD a little hobby-horse,
    And it was dapple gray,
Its head was made of pea-straw,
    Its tail was made of hay.

Hey diddle diddle,
The cat and the fiddle,
The cow jumped over the moon;
    The little dog laughed
    To see such sport,
And the dish ran away with the spoon.

© THE PLATT & MUNK CO. INC.

© THE PLATT & MUNK CO. INC.

THE CATS went out to serenade,
And on a banjo sweetly played;
And summer nights they climbed
    a tree
And sang, "My love, oh, come to me!"

I'M GLAD the sky is painted blue,
And earth is painted green,
With such a lot of nice fresh air
All sandwiched in between.

JACK SPRAT could eat no fat,
    His wife could eat no lean;
And so betwixt them both, you see,
    They licked the platter clean.

WEE Willie Winkie
    Runs through the town,
Upstairs and downstairs,
    In his nightgown;
Rapping at the window,
    Crying through the lock,
"Are the children in their beds,
    For now it's eight o'clock?"

I LOVE you well, my little brother,
    And you are fond of me;
Let us be kind to one another,
    As brothers ought to be.
You shall learn to play with me,
    And learn to use my toys;
And then I think that we shall be
    Two happy little boys.

Peter, Peter, pumpkin-eater,
    Had a wife, and couldn't keep her;
He put her in a pumpkin shell,
    And there he kept her very well.

BAA, BAA, black sheep,
    Have you any wool?
Yes, sir, yes, sir,
    Three bags full.
One for the master,
    One for the dame,
And one for the little boy
    Who lives in the lane.

OLD King Cole was a merry old soul,
And a merry old soul was he;
He called for his pipe, and he called
    for his bowl,
And he called for his fiddlers three.
And every fiddler, he had a fine fiddle,
And a very fine fiddle had he;
"Tweedle dee, tweedle dee,"
    said the fiddlers;
"Oh, there's none so rare
    as can compare
With Cole and his fiddlers three."

HICKORY, dickory, dock,
The mouse ran up the clock.
The clock struck one,
    And down he ran;
Hickory, dickory, dock.

DAFFY-down-dilly has come
    up to town,
In a yellow petticoat and
    a green gown.

LITTLE Robin Redbreast sat upon a tree,
Up went Pussy-cat, and down went he.
Down came Pussy-cat, and away
    Robin ran;
Said little Robin Redbreast,
    "Catch me if you can."

THERE were two blackbirds
    Sitting on a hill.
The one named Jack,
    And the other named Jill.
Fly away, Jack!
Fly away, Jill!
Come again, Jack!
Come again, Jill!

A SUNSHINY shower
Won't last half an hour.

To market, to market, to buy a fat pig.
    Home again, home again, jiggety-jig;
To market, to market, to buy a fat hog,
    Home again, home again, jiggety-jog.

© THE PLATT & MUNK CO. INC.

MISTRESS Mary,
  Quite contrary,
  How does your garden grow?
  With silver bells,
  And cockleshells,
And pretty maids all in a row.

THERE was a little girl who had
    a little curl
  Right in the middle of her
    forehead;
When she was good, she was very,
    very good,
  And when she was bad, she was
    horrid.

LADYBUG, ladybug,
Fly away home,
Your house is on fire,
Your children are gone.
All but one, and her name is Ann;
She crept under the pudding-pan.

OH, DEAR, what can the matter be?
  Johnny's so long at the fair.
He promised to buy me a bunch of
    blue ribbons
  To tie up my bonny brown hair.

DOCTOR Foster went to Gloster,
In a shower of rain;
He stepped in a puddle,
Up to the middle,
And never went there again.

MARY had a pretty bird,
  Feathers bright and yellow,
Slender legs—upon my word,
  He was a pretty fellow.

Jack and Jill went up the hill,
  To fetch a pail of water;
Jack fell down and broke his crown,
  And Jill came tumbling after.

DEEDLE, deedle, dumpling,
My son John
Went to bed with his stockings on;
One shoe off, and one shoe on,
Deedle, deedle, dumpling,
My son John.

LITTLE Boy Blue, come blow your horn;
    The sheep's in the meadow,
    The cow's in the corn.
Where's the little boy who looks
    after the sheep?
He's under the haystack, fast asleep.
Will you wake him? No, not I;
For if I do, he'll be sure to cry.

AS I was going to St. Ives,
    I met a man with seven wives,
    Every wife had seven sacks,
    Every sack had seven cats,
    Every cat had seven kits:
Kits, cats, sacks, and wives,
How many were there going
    to St. Ives?

PUSSY-CAT, Pussy-cat where have
    you been?
I've been to London to visit
    the Queen.
Pussy-cat, Pussy-cat, what did
    you there?
I frightened a little mouse under
    her chair.

BOBBY SHAFTOE'S gone to sea,
Silver buckles on his knee;
He'll come back and marry me,
    Pretty Bobby Shaftoe.

Bobby Shaftoe's fat and fair,
Combing down his yellow hair,
He's my love for evermore;
    Pretty Bobby Shaftoe.

Hippety hop to the barber shop,
    To get a stick of candy,
One for you and one for me,
    And one for Sister Mandy.

© THE PLATT & MUNK CO. INC.

© THE PLATT & MUNK CO. INC.

TWO LITTLE dogs
Sat by the fire,
   Over a fender of coal-dust.
Said one little dog
To the other little dog,
   If you don't talk, why, I must.
   1, 2, 3, 4, 5!
I caught a hare alive
   6, 7, 8, 9, 10!
I let him go again.

RIDE a cock-horse to Banbury Cross
To see a fine lady upon a
   white horse;
Rings on her fingers and bells on
   her toes,
She shall have music wherever
   she goes.

LITTLE Jack Horner
Sat in a corner,
Eating a Christmas pie;
He put in his thumb,
And pulled out a plum,
And said, "What a good boy am I!"

POLLY, put the kettle on,
Polly, put the kettle on,
Polly, put the kettle on,
   We'll all have tea.

Sukey, take it off again,
Sukey, take it off again,
Sukey, take it off again,
   They've all gone away.

ONCE I saw a little bird
   Come hop, hop, hop;
And I cried, "Little bird,
   Will you stop, stop, stop?"
I was going to the window
   To say, "How do you do?"
But he shook his little tail,
   And away he flew.

Old Mother Hubbard went to the cupboard,
   To get her poor dog a bone;
But when she got there, the cupboard was bare
   And so the poor dog had none.

SIMPLE Simon met a pieman
    Going to the fair;
Said Simple Simon to the pieman,
    "Let me taste your ware."
Said the pieman to Simple Simon,
    "Show me first your penny;"
Said Simple Simon to the pieman
    "Indeed I have not any."
Simple Simon went a-fishing,
    For to catch a whale;
All the water he had got
    Was in his mother's pail.

RUB-a-dub-dub,
Three men in a tub,
And who do you think they be?
The butcher, the baker,
The candle-stick maker,
They've all gone off on a spree.

Three little kittens,
They lost their mittens,
And they began to cry,
    "Oh! mummy dear,
    We sadly fear,
    Our mittens we have lost!"
"What! lost your mittens,
You naughty kittens,
    Then you shall have no pie."
    Miew, miew, miew, miew,
    Miew, miew, miew, miew.

The three little kittens,
They found their mittens,
And they began to cry,
    "Oh! mummy dear,
    See here, see here,
    Our mittens we have found."
"What! found your mittens,
You little kittens,
    Then you shall have some pie."
    Purr, purr, purr, purr,
    Purr, purr, purr, purr.

A CAT came fiddling out of a barn
With a pair of bagpipes under her
    arm.
She could sing nothing but fiddle cum
    fee,
The mouse has married the bumble-
    bee;
Pipe, cat—dance, mouse,
We'll have a wedding at our fine house.

© THE PLATT & MUNK CO. INC.

BLOW, wind, blow! and go, mill, go!
That the miller may grind his corn;
   That the baker may take it,
   And into rolls make it,
And bring us some hot in the morn.

TOM, he was a piper's son,
He learnt to play when he was young,
And all the tune that he could play,
Was, "Over the hills and far away!"

THE MAN in the Moon looked out of
      the moon,
Looked out of the moon and said,
"'Tis time for all children on the earth
To think about getting to bed!"

FOR every evil under the sun,
There is a remedy, or there is none,
If there be one, try and find it;
If there be none, never mind it.

London Bridge is falling down,
   Falling down, falling down,
London Bridge is falling down,
   My fair lady.

MARY had a little lamb,
   Its fleece was white as snow;
And everywhere that Mary went
   The lamb was sure to go.
It followed her to school one day,
   Which was against the rule,
It made the children laugh and play,
   To see a lamb at school.

LITTLE Miss Muffet
Sat on a tuffet,
Eating of curds and whey;
  There came a spider,
  And sat down beside her,
And frightened Miss Muffet away.

THIRTY days hath September,
April, June, and November;
All the rest have thirty-one—
Except February, alone
Which has four and twenty-four,
And every fourth year, one day more.

GEORGEY Porgey, pudding and pie,
Kissed the girls and made them cry;
When the girls came out to play,
Georgey Porgey ran away.

LITTLE WIND, blow on the hill top;
Little wind, blow down the plain;
Little wind, blow up the sunshine;
Little wind, blow off the rain.

PAT-A-CAKE, pat-a-cake, baker's man.
Bake me a cake as fast as you can.
Pat it and prick it, and mark it with B,
And put in the oven for baby and me.

I LIKE little pussy,
  Her coat is so warm,
And if I don't hurt her,
  She'll do me no harm;
So I'll not pull her tail,
  Nor drive her away,
But pussy and I
  Very gently will play.

RAIN, rain, go away,
Come again another day.
Little Johnny wants to play.

Ding, dong, bell,
Pussy's in the well.
Who put her in?
Little Johnny Green.
Who pulled her out?
Little Tommy Stout.

© THE PLATT & MUNK CO., INC.

HUMPTY-Dumpty sat on a wall,
Humpty-Dumpty had a great fall,
All the King's horses,
And all the King's men,
Couldn't put Humpty together again.

THIS little pig went to market;
This little pig stayed at home;
This little pig had roast beef,
This little pig had none;
And this little pig cried,
"Wee-wee-wee-wee-wee!"
        All the way home.

THE QUEEN of Hearts
She made some tarts,
    All on a summer's day.
The Knave of Hearts,
He stole the tarts,
    And took them clean away.

LITTLE drops of water,
    Little grains of sand,
Make the mighty ocean,
    And the pleasant land.

COCK crows in the morn
    To tell us to rise,
And he who lies late
    Will never be wise;
For early to bed,
    And early to rise,
Is the way to be healthy
    And wealthy and wise.

A DILLER, a dollar,
A ten o'clock scholar,
What makes you come so soon?
You used to come at ten o'clock,
But now you come at noon.

There was an old woman
Who lived in a shoe,
She had so many children
She didn't know what to do.
She gave them some broth
Without any bread,
Then kissed them all soundly
And put them to bed.

© THE PLATT & MUNK CO., INC.

Animal Stories

Illustrated by Wesley Dennis

What a Beautiful Cow and Calf!

The little black dog has come to say "Good morning" to the pretty calf and its mother, the cow.

They all live on a big farm. In the summer the cow and her baby spend the days in the pasture. There is tender, green grass for them to eat. In the brook there is clear water for them to drink. When winter comes, cows live in snug, warm barns.

Now they eat hay. Hay is the grass which the farmer lets grow tall in the summer. When it is very high he cuts it down and lets it dry in the sun. Next he piles it up in big stacks. These are called haystacks.

When the wind and sun have dried the hay, it is time to take it in.

It is tossed up on a big wagon. Then it is taken to the barn to be stored. It will make many good winter meals for our friends, the cows.

What good friends they are! Cows give us the good, nourishing milk we drink. When we have cereal for breakfast, think how strange it would taste without milk! And think how good the butter tastes on our bread!

We must thank the cow for these good things. Butter is made from milk. Without milk we would have no butter. Without milk we would not grow healthy and strong.

There are many different kinds of cows. Some are all black. Others are black and white. Still others are brown. Some cows have horns and others have none. Our pretty cow in the picture is called a Guernsey. A Guernsey cow gives very rich milk.

What fun it would be to live on a dairy farm where there are many cows and calves! We would see the big pans where the cream forms on top of the milk. We would see the electric churn where butter is made. We might even have a piece of bread with sweet, fresh butter spread on it and a glass of cold milk to drink. We could watch, too, while the milk was put on big trucks in shining cans or bottles to be shipped to the city. What a fine gift from our friends, the cows!

© THE PLATT & MUNK CO. INC.

Five Purring Kittens - Three White

Don't you wish these five soft, purring kittens belonged to you? Of all the pets a girl or boy could have, none is so graceful or light on its feet as a kitten. Watch kittens when they are at play. They make no noise when they tumble about. They have soft cushions on their paws. But they have sharp claws, too, and if they are hurt or angry or frightened, they will arch their backs and they may scratch.

Always be kind to your kitten, and it will not scratch you.

Kittens spend most of their days playing. They love to roll about in tissue paper or to jump on it to hear it crackle. When they are tired, they roll up in soft little balls and go to sleep.

Have you ever heard a kitten purr? It is a soft, happy sound. It is a lovely little rumble that comes from deep down inside the kitten's

A Black and a Yellow

chest. This means the kitten is happy and content. Just hold him gently and stroke him. Soon you will hear him purr.

There are many kinds of cats. Have you ever seen a Manx cat? This animal actually has no tail! It was born that way. And its hind legs are much longer than its front legs. Then there are the Siamese cats. They have beautiful blue eyes, light tan coats, and black paws. We know best the tame, gentle pussy-cat that curls up beside the fire or rubs against the chair leg when it is coaxing for something.

But there are wild, fierce cousins of the cat, too, like the lion and tiger. Then there is another wild cousin, the cheetah, trained in Asia to hunt wild game.

Would you like to have a cheetah for a pet? The five pretty kittens in the picture would be much more fun to own. Don't you think so?

Mother Pig and Her Babies

This mother pig and her five baby piglets are very happy together in the shade of the big tree. Mother pig does not look too friendly, though, does she? She does not want us to come too close to her babies. She does not want them to be frightened.

Pigs are not always as clean as many other farm animals. You see, pigs are fed to make them very fat. When the sun shines down on the farm, it makes pigs very hot. So we cannot blame them if they like to lie down in the nice cool mud to cool off, can we?

On a fine farm you will see pigs that look as clean as those in the picture. A pig does not do much but eat and sleep. The farmer feeds it a great deal. When the pig is nice and fat, the farmer takes it to market. Bacon and pork chops and ham all come from the pig. Even the hide of a pig is very useful to us. Beautiful purses are made of pigskin.

Do you see how blunt the pigs' noses are? A pig's nose is called a snout. Our barnyard pigs today do not have to root in the ground for their food. Perhaps some of them like to. But a long time ago all pigs were wild and had to root or dig for their food. With such a blunt, tough snout that was easy to do.

Pigs like water to drink, but they are afraid of deep water. They will not go near a lake or river. They are even afraid of a deep brook. Can you guess why? A pig cannot swim. The reason for this is strange. Its legs are short. Its hoofs are sharp. The pig's throat is very fat. If it tries to swim, its sharp hoofs may cut its throat. Aren't they wise, then, to stay away from deep water? Mother pig knows that she and her babies are safe under the big tree.

In some countries of Europe, Asia and Africa can be found a very fierce, wild pig called the wild boar. It is not at all like our sleepy barnyard pig.

When tiny piglets feel happy they dance around in circles. Watch them sometime. It is a pretty sight.

© THE PLATT & MUNK CO. INC.

Big Sheep, Woolly Sheep, Where

See this beautiful sheep, standing in the green meadow! He looks very proud and fierce with his great horns. You see, his horns have been trimmed so he cannot hurt anyone.

The father sheep is called a ram. The mother sheep is a ewe. And the baby sheep? Of course – it is a lamb.

Sheep wear a very heavy coat of wool. The wool has still another name – fleece. Once a year the farmer clips the sheeps' wool. He washes it well to free it of dust and bits of grass and burs. Then he sends it off to the mill where it is washed again and woven into cloth.

Think of all the pretty things we have that are made of wool! Many fine sweaters and snow suits and warm blankets are made of wool. Sheep do not mind having their coats clipped. It does not hurt them at all – not any more than it hurts

Are You Going?

you to have your hair cut.

Even so, a sheep is not at all brave. A leaf or a little piece of paper blowing across the meadow will make him run. And if one sheep runs, the whole flock of sheep runs after him. Isn't that silly? Sometimes a frightened sheep falls over a rough spot in the meadow. The next one follows, and the next and the next.

That is why farmers have sheep dogs. One of these clever dogs can always run around a flock of frightened sheep and quiet them. Soon they are busy nibbling grass again. You see what a good friend to man the sheep dog is.

There are flocks of sheep in most of the countries of the world. Long ago, in Bible times, we are told, a rich man was the man with a large flock of sheep. Even today that is true in some parts of the world. Some of the biggest flocks of sheep are raised in our western states.

The Dog Is My Good Friend

What is so beautiful as a fine dog? Have you one of your own? If you have, you have a wonderful friend. He may be a little black Scotty, or he may be a collie with a white ruff around his neck. Or he may not be of any well-known breed, but that does not matter. A good dog is one of the best friends a girl or boy can have.

The dogs in the picture are a pointer and an English setter. The pointer, with his brown spots, has short hair and a pointed tail. The setter is shaggy haired. Pointers and setters love to run and hunt and so are happier in the country than in the city.

Long ago dogs were used in Holland, Germany, and Belgium to pull little carts of vegetables and milk to market.

In the Far North, where the Eskimos live, dogs are used to draw sleds across the snow. They are very strong and run many miles from one village to another. They are called the express trains of the Arctic.

In the city we sometimes see a big dog leading a man who cannot see. This dog has been carefully trained to watch the green and red traffic lights. He knows just when to cross the busy street so his master will not be hurt.

On the big sheep ranches in the West, what would the farmers do without dogs? Clever dogs keep sheep from straying. They are guardians of the sheep. They are the farmers' best friend.

Your dog has a keen sense of smell. If you are lost, he can find you. If you are in danger, he will bark and bark until help comes. Always be kind to your dog, for he loves you very much. Be sure always to have a bowl of water where your dog can reach it. Dogs must have plenty of water. When you throw a stick or a ball, teach your dog to bring it back to you. Then always pat his head to show him he has pleased you.

Never tease him, for that may make him cross. And always let your dog know you are his friend as he is yours. Then what fun you can have together!

© THE PLATT & MUNK CO. INC.

The Chicken Family, the Happiest

The rooster, with his shining feathers and his handsome red comb, loves to strut across the barnyard. He seems to be saying, "See what a fine fellow I am!"

The little red hen is much too busy looking after her chicks to think much of herself. If she is saying anything, it is, "Now hurry, hurry, children! I have a nice, fat worm for you! Mind your manners, no pushing!" The fine worm is an extra treat for the little chicks. They have had a good meal of warm mash which the farmer's wife gives them each morning.

A few days ago, every one of these little chicks lived inside an egg. Mother Hen had sat on the eggs for twenty-one days to keep them safe and warm. Then, when the chicks had grown big enough, they

in the Barnyard

pecked the shells of the eggs until they opened. Out stepped the little yellow chicks. How proud of them Mother Hen was!

There are more than a hundred different kinds of chickens in the world. Did you know that? The ones we see in the picture are called Rhode Island Reds. There are beautiful, snowy white chickens called White Leghorns. The Black Giant has black feathers and very long legs. You should see it run across the barnyard! It can go like the wind.

Some chickens lay brown eggs and some lay white eggs. But they both taste the same. When Mother poaches an egg for your breakfast, doesn't it taste good?

The little chickens say "Peep, peep, peep," as they run about the barnyard. Sometimes Mother Hen seems to sing a happy tune. That is when she has laid a fine egg for your breakfast.

When we hear the red rooster sing out "Cock-a-doodle-do" early in the morning, we know a new day has begun. Far off another rooster will answer, "Cock-a-doodle-do."

© THE PLATT & MUNK CO. INC.

Donkeys at Work and at Play

When you first look at donkeys, like the mother and baby donkey here, they seem to be very much like horses. But donkeys are different in many ways.

A donkey is a very strong animal. It can do much heavier work than a horse. Some donkeys are very small. These donkeys are called burros. Girls and boys like burros for pets. A burro will draw a cart or give a boy or girl a ride on its back.

A donkey or burro cannot go as fast as a horse. But it can go where a horse would not dare to go. It is never afraid to go up a steep mountain. It knows just where to put its little hoofs, and it never slips. It carries its load up to the top.

Did you ever hear that a donkey is stubborn? Do you know what that means? It means that it will do only what it wants to do. It will not go when you tell it to. But perhaps there is a reason for this. Maybe somebody has been unkind to it.

A donkey is not dainty about food. A horse will nibble only fresh grass. It wants plenty of oats and mash. A donkey will eat grass that is dry and not very tasty. But it does want plenty of good, clean, cold water.

In Italy and Spain the donkey does much of the hard work for the farmer. Out on a country road there you may see something strange coming along. You may wonder, for it looks very much like a haystack! But how can a haystack move along the road? Then you see little hoofs moving along under it. Now you know. It is a burro carrying a load bigger than it is!

Have you ever seen a donkey in the circus? When hitched to a little wagon, he will pull a clown around the ring to make the boys and girls laugh. He has a good time.

The Wild Ducks in the Marsh Are

These fine, wild ducks are cousins of the barnyard ducks. But instead of living in a little pen near the brook, they live on rivers and in the wood. The barnyard duck eats grain and mash which the farmer's wife gives it. The wild duck makes a meal of small fish and wild grain it finds in the wood. When winter comes, it flies south where it is warm.

You would think it might be hard for such a heavy bird to fly very far. But remember, it has strong wings. It can alight on either land or water. The father duck is called a drake. His feathers are of several lovely, bright colors.

Ducks have two other cousins. Can you guess who they are? One is the goose. The other is the swan. Both the goose and the swan have very long necks. The duck's neck is short.

a Lovely Splash of Color

Birds like ducks, chickens, geese, and turkeys are called fowl. All fowl that spend much of their time in water have feet that are different from those of fowl that stay on land. Have you ever looked at a duck's feet? You will find they have a thick layer of skin stretched between their toes, like little webs. Web-feet act just like little paddles to help ducks swim. Ducks would rather be in the water than on the rough ground.

Do you wonder why ducks do not get wet when they dive for fish? Under their tail feathers they have a tiny pocket filled with oil. They dip their bills into this little pocket and spread the oil on their feathers. This makes the feathers waterproof.

We learn a lesson from this. Sometimes when Father is going to a marsh where he may get his feet wet, he puts oil on his boots.

We call two ducks a "brace" of ducks. How fine for Christmas dinner!

How Nimble the Goats Are!

What a good time these goats are having! A goat is not a beautiful animal but it is nimble on its feet. No mountain peak is too high or too slippery for a goat. It can climb in places that no man could possibly reach. It is never afraid.

Little goats are playful. They love to dance and prance about and butt each other with their hard little heads. They like to nibble grass, but they will eat almost anything.

In Belgium and France you will often see a little herd of goats trotting along the road. Jungle, jingle, jingle, go the bells on their collars. Tap, tap, go their little hoofs. Beside them walks a boy or girl, keeping them all together on the road.

Here and there a house door will open. The good wife will come out with a pitcher in her hand. The goats will stop. The boy or girl leading the herd will milk one of the goats. Quick as a wink the pitcher is full. What an easy way to get good, fresh milk! How good it is!

Fine cheese is made of goats' milk. Ask Mother to make you a sandwich of goats' milk cheese. See how good it tastes. Perhaps you would even like a glass of goats' milk. It has a flavor quite different from cows' milk.

Did you ever hear of the Angora goat? It has larger horns than other kinds of goats and it has a lovely silky coat. On some farms there are big herds of Angora goats. Farmers raise them for their fine wool coats. So many beautiful things are made from this wool. Perhaps you have a pair of Angora mittens that feel just like kittens' fur. Or Mother may have knit an Angora sweater for you.

When you wear either the mittens or the sweater, you will be reminded of the frisky little goats playing on the mountain top.

Sometimes boys and girls who live in the country have a pet goat. They hitch it with a pretty red harness to a little wagon and drive it all over.

© THE PLATT & MUNK CO. INC.

A Turkey in the Wildwood and

The big turkey gobbler we see strutting across the farm is always thought of as the Thanksgiving turkey. But long before the Pilgrims celebrated their first Thanksgiving Day, wild turkeys lived in America. We still can see some wild turkeys in the woods. They have feathers even more beautiful than those of the turkeys that strut through the barnyard.

Do you know how the wild turkey got its name? We think it came from the name the Indians gave to this big bird, "firkee." Perhaps the Pilgrims who came from England did not hear it spoken properly. They called it "turkey."

The Indians used the wild turkey for food. They used the largest feathers for their arrows. They stuck the finest feathers in their hair.

The wild turkey must keep on the watch for its enemies. One of these

A Turkey in the Field

enemies is the great horned owl. Another is the fox – the sly red fox or the gray one.

The barnyard turkey grows fatter than the wild turkey. It has good corn to eat. At night it sleeps in a coop. Here it is safe from both the owl and the fox. When it rains, the farmer does not let the little turkeys get wet.

When you have your Thanksgiving dinner, your turkey is not yet a year old. A wild turkey lives to be five years old or even more.

On Thanksgiving Day let us remember the Pilgrims. Think how hard it was for the Pilgrim father to get a turkey. He had to watch out for Indians. He had to watch out for wolves and bears. But he brought home a turkey for his boys and girls. They had a grand feast. They were thankful. And we should be thankful, too, for all our blessings.

Let Us Look at Beautiful Horses

The new baby horse, resting near its mother in the warm barn, has a visitor. It is the big red rooster.

A gentle horse will love to have you feed it bits of food. It will enjoy apples and carrots and lumps of sugar.

A baby horse is called a foal or a colt. Its mother is called a mare. This little colt with the white star on its forehead is only a few days old. It looks like a thoroughbred. When it grows up, it may win prizes for jumping in the big horse show. Or it may carry its owner on long rides in the country.

There are horses of many kinds. Not so long ago horses did most of the work on the farm. Today that work is done mostly by machines. In the cities, where now we see many trucks and automobiles, horses used to pull the delivery wagons. They worked very hard, indeed.

Before we had automobiles to ride in, it was fun to drive a gentle horse hitched to a buggy. In the winter, horses pulled sleighs. But you could not go as far on a trip as you can in an automobile today. Your horse would grow too tired.

This little colt and its mother will go out in the fields pretty soon and nibble the fresh, green grass. Just now they are enjoying their stall in the stable. The floor has a thick covering of sweet, clean hay to make a soft, comfortable bed.

When the little colt is older it will be taken to the blacksmith. The blacksmith will put iron shoes on its hoofs to protect them. When a horse has had shoes put on, we say it is shod.

Every morning the stableman will brush both the mother's and the baby's coats until they shine. Then he will brush and comb the long silky hair that grows on the mother's neck. This is called a mane. Baby's mane has not grown out yet. The little colt's legs are long and unsteady at first. It does not try to run. But soon it will be running in the meadow with the other colts. What a happy life for this mother and her baby!

© THE PLATT & MUNK CO. INC.